SING A

Edited by MICH

Set

1. RED RIVER VALLEY

American traditional
arr. Jan Holdstock

1. From this valley they say you are going,
   I shall miss your sweet face and your smile.
   Just because you are weary and tired,
   You are changing your range for a while.
   Chorus

2. When you think of the valley you're leaving,
   Oh how lonely and drear it would be.
   When you think of the fond heart you're breaking
   And the pain you are causing to me.
   Chorus

The Chorus is sung in two parts as written. The verse takes its tune from the top line of the Chorus, and the second part is hummed.

2. WHEN THE SAINTS GO MARCHING IN

American traditional
arr. Jan Holdstock

3. BUFFALO BOY

American traditional
arr. Jan Holdstock

2. How will you come to the wedding,
   Dear old Buffalo Boy?
   I'm gonna come in my ox-cart,
   That's if the weather be good!

3. What will you wear to the wedding,
   Dear old Buffalo Boy?
   I'm gonna wear all my old clothes,
   That's if the weather be good!

4. Who will you bring to the wedding,
   Dear old Buffalo Boy?
   I'm gonna bring all my chickens,
   That's if the weather be good!

5. There ain't gonna be no wedding!
   So long, old Buffalo Boy!

*Melody (2nd voices)
2. I'm gonna come by ox-cart,
3. I'm gonna wear my old clothes,
4. I'm gonna bring my chickens,

4. SILVER TRUMPET

American traditional
arr. Elaine Gregory

1. Well I've ne-ver been to Heav'n, but I've been told
2. If re - li-gion were a thing that mon-ey could buy, —
3. Well now, if you want a sil - ver trum-pet like mine —

Hand down that trum-pet, send down that trum-pet,

Hand me down my sil - ver trum-pet, Gab - ri - el,
The
The
You'd

gates are made of pearl and the streets are made of gold.
rich would live and the poor would die.
bet - ter learn to play it in plen - ty of time.

Hand down that trum-pet, send down that trum-pet,

Hand me down my sil-ver trum-pet, Lord. Oh hand me down, Oh hand me

Oh hand me down,

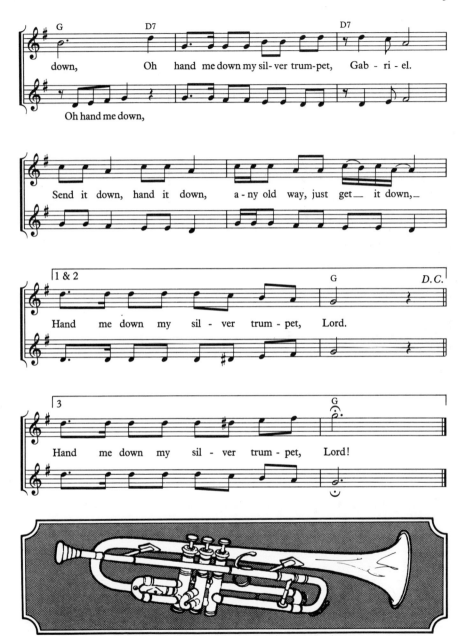

down, Oh hand me down my sil-ver trum-pet, Gab-ri-el.

Oh hand me down,

Send it down, hand it down, a-ny old way, just get__ it down,__

1 & 2

Hand me down my sil-ver trum-pet, Lord.

3

Hand me down my sil-ver trum-pet, Lord!

5. WHEN JOSHUA WALK ROUND JERICHO

West Indian traditional
arr. Jan Holdstock

2. When shall my labour have an end,
   To shout 'Hallelujah' and the walls fall down?
   When shall the Lamb of God descend,
   To shout 'Hallelujah' and the walls fall down?
   In the morning, in the morning,
   In the morning, soldiers of the cross.
   In the morning, in the morning,
   He shout 'Hallelujah' and the walls fall down.

6. HAUL AWAY, JOE

English traditional
arr. Ken Lee

2. Way, haul away, the packet is a-rollin'.
Chorus *Way, haul away, etc.*

3. Way, haul away, we'll hang and haul together.
Chorus

4. Way, haul away, we'll haul for better weather.
Chorus

5. Geordie Charlton had a pig, and it was double jointed.
Chorus

6. He took it to the blacksmith's shop to get its trotters pointed.
Chorus

7. King Louis was the king o' France before the Revolution.
Chorus

8. King Louis got his head cut off, and spoiled his Constitution.
Chorus

9. Way, haul away, we'll haul away the bowlin'.
Chorus

7. O SINNER MAN

Anon.
arr. Pat Broderick

1. O sinner man, where you gon-na run to? O sinner man, where you gon-na run to? O sinner man, where you gon-na run to? All on that day.

*O sinner man, *O sinner man, *O sinner man, man,

All verses: All on that day,

2. Run to the rocks; rocks won't you hide me?

3. Run to the sea; sea was a-boiling.

4. Run to the sky; sky was a-falling.

5. O sinner man, where you gonna run to?

*2nd voices

2. Run to the rocks,
3. Run to the sea,
4. Run to the sky,

8. AN ERISKAY LOVE LILT

Scottish traditional
arr. Ken Lee

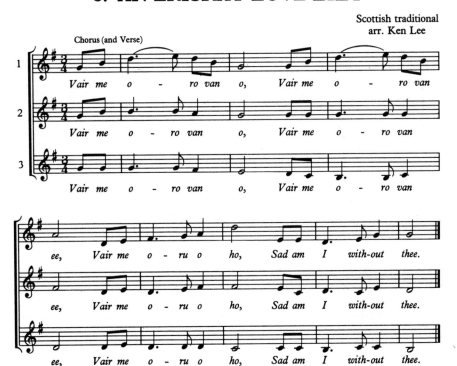

Top part: sings words for verses.

Lower voices: hum or sing softly to an open vowel sound.

All parts: sing words in the chorus.

Chorus

1. When I'm lonely, dear white heart,
Black the night or wild the sea,
By love's light my foot finds
The old pathway to thee.
Chorus

2. Thou'rt the music of my heart,
Harp of joy, oh cruit mo chridh,*
Moon of guidance by night,
Strength and light thou'rt to me.
Chorus

* Cruit mo chridh: harp of my heart (pronounced crootch mo chree)

9. DE BATTLE OB JERICHO

Spiritual
arr. Elaine Gregory

(Verse 3)

(3.) Iam ram sheep horns be-gan to blow, And the trumpets be-gan to— soun',——

Josh-ua com-mand - ed the child-ren to SHOUT! And de walls came tum-bling
Then he told

down.—— Josh-ua fit de bat -tle ob— Jer - i - cho,——

p Chorus

Jer - i - cho,—— Jer - i - cho,———— Josh-ua fit de bat -tle ob—

Jer - i - cho,— And de walls came tum - bling dow - nnnn.

10. SWING LOW, SWEET CHARIOT

Spiritual
arr. Donald Hughes

*This phrase, and its equivalent on the next line, may be effectively sung by solo voice, with general chorus interjections of 'Coming for to carry me home.'

11. THERE'S A HOLE IN MY BUCKET

English/American traditional
arr. Jan Holdstock

Use any or all of the 3 extra parts with the tune.

2. *Then mend* it dear Henry	3. *With what* shall I mend it ?
4. With *a straw*, dear Henry	5. The straw is *too long* !
6. *Then cut* it, dear Henry	7. *With what* shall I cut it ?
8. With *an axe*, dear Henry	9. The axe is *too dull*.
10. *Then hone* it, dear Henry	11. *With what* shall I hone it ?
12. With *a stone*, dear Henry	13. The stone is *too dry*.
14. *Then wet* it, dear Henry	15. *With what* shall I wet it ?
16. *With water*, dear Henry	17. *With what* shall I fetch it ?
18. In *a bucket*, dear Henry	19. There's *a hole* in my bucket.

Words in italics can be used for the last two notes of each verse in the accompanying parts.

12. PRETTY GIRL

Words by
Michael Stocks

Roumanian traditional
arr. Michael Stocks

1. Since I met you,— pretty girl, Can't for-get you, pretty girl,
Now we're part-ed, pretty girl, Bro-ken heart-ed, pretty girl.

1. Since I met you, pretty girl, Can't for-get you,— pretty girl,
Now we are part - ed, Bro-ken heart - ed, pretty girl.

1. Since I met you, pretty girl, Can't for-get you, pretty girl,
Now we're part-ed, pretty girl, Bro-ken heart - ed, pretty girl.

2. How I've missed you, pretty girl,
Never kissed you, pretty girl.
Since I met you, pretty girl,
Can't forget you, pretty girl.

13. BRING A TORCH

A Christmas Carol

Words by
G. Hitchcock

French traditional
arr. Michael Stocks

2. Gently now, Jeanette, Isabella,
Gently now, the babe is asleep.
See the brightness around him shining,
Gleaming on ox and ass and sheep.
Come, come, come see the fairest maiden,
Come, come, come see the fairest son.

3. Sing noel, Jeanette, Isabella,
Softly sing noel, everyone.
Angels high in the heavens are singing,
Peace on the earth, God's will be done.
Sleep, sleep, sleep 'til the dawn awakens,
Sleep, sleep, sleep little infant King.

ACKNOWLEDGEMENTS

No. 6   Melody and words from the *Shanty Book Part 1* (R.R. Terry) by permission of J. Curwen & Sons Ltd, London

No. 8   Melody and words from *Songs of the Hebrides* by permission of Boosey & Hawkes Music Publishers Ltd

No. 13   Words © 1960 H. Freedman & Co. and reproduced by permission of EMI Music Publishing Ltd

Reproduced and printed by Halstan & Co. Ltd., Amersham, Bucks., England